CU00406124

The Delectable Book of Dilemmas

First published in Great Britain in 1999
by André Deutsch Limited
76 Dean Street
London W1V 5HA

www.vci.co.uk

André Deutsch is a VCI plc company

2 4 6 8 10 9 7 5 3 1

A catalogue record for this book is available from the British Library

ISBN 0 233 99613 3

Typeset by Derek Doyle & Associates, Mold, Flintshire.
Printed by WSOY, Finland.

The Delectable Book of Dilemmas

Sarah Toynbee and Charlie Hurt

ANDRE DEUTSCH

To our best friends

We have compiled a list of dilemmas. There are not necessarily any right or wrong answers; we leave them to you. In order to avoid tedious repetition, we have slanted many of the questions at 'him' or 'her', though most are interchangeable.

Your husband announces he is infatuated with another woman but that a brief affair will get her out of his system and normal service will be resumed. Do you agree? What if he is in love with another man?

Your wife announces she is in love with another man but that a brief affair will get him out of her system and normal service will be resumed. Do you agree? What if she is in love with another woman?

Your new husband tells you that he once committed date rape but was cleared at trial some years ago. Do you leave him? Do you report him?

Your husband tells you he is involved with a huge fraud, from which you have already unwittingly benefited. What do you do?

The police suspect your wife of involvement in a serious and nasty crime but although people have been hurt no one has died. The police have no evidence. You find the incriminating document. Do you tear it up? Do you give it to the police?

Would you pull the wings off a butterfly for a fantastic holiday? Or shoot but only wound a hare? Or flush your child's hamster down the lavatory? What if you had to own up to your actions?

You are offered twenty years of utter happiness but will die on the final day. Would you take them? What if you had to commit suicide?

You discover that your loved one has been secretly having an affair with your best friend. Who would you reject: your loved one, your friend, both or neither?

At odds of 9 to 1 against losing your life, would you play Russian roulette for £1 million? What about 5 to 1? What about £500,000? What if your death would save the life of a child?

Would you like your loved one to be cleverer and/or more attractive than you?

For your annual income, would you go three months without washing or cleaning your teeth? You would have to continue your normal life, going to work and attending parties and so on, and would not be able to explain your predicament to anyone.

Would you choose a wonderfully happy life and die at 50, or be tolerably content but not totally fulfilled until 80?

Would you have your right index finger chopped off in return for a guarantee that you would never contract a major disease? What about your thumb and forefinger? What about your right hand?

Would you walk 1,000 yards naked down a busy street in return for £10,000 towards your favourite charity? You would not be in danger of physical harm, but would not be able to explain your action to anyone. What if the money was coming to you?

In order to ensure a full attendance at your own funeral, would you arrange that your best friend had no one at hers?

A scurrilous story about you is doing the rounds, though in truth it happened to your best friend. Do you set the record straight? What about the other way round?

You can land the job of your dreams by cheating a more able and needy candidate without being found out. Would you do so?

Would you surrender ten years of your life for: superb looks, irresistible charm, dazzling intelligence, or fabulous wealth?

If you were sent your obituary, prematurely written by your close friends and colleagues at work, would you open the envelope and read it?

You discover that a beloved married friend is having an affair. She begs you not to tell her husband, an even dearer friend. Do you? Does the sex of the adulterer influence your decision?

Would you like to know the date of your death?

Would you give up your favourite pastime for five years to provide for 100 starving children for the same period?

You can have one soulmate and confidante but no other good friends, or several good friends but no soulmate. Which would you choose?

Would you put in four weeks' unpaid overtime to avoid a month's sunshine holiday with your parents-in-law?

Would you watch a public execution on television?

You are stuck in an underground lift with a stranger. You know you will not be released for 30 hours but only have enough oxygen for the two of you for 25 hours. You both have similarly happy lives and expectations, but you have a pistol. Do you kill yourself or your companion, both of you or neither of you?

Would you accept the equivalent of your annual income from a tabloid newspaper for damaging information about an acquaintance you don't particularly like? Would you accept £1 million for severely damaging information about a good friend? What if you were to be quoted?

For £1 million would you, without explanation, never communicate again in any way with your best friend?

You are driving a car while over the alcohol limit and hit a pizza delivery boy on his bike. You don't think he is badly hurt but are not sure. To fail a breath test would mean losing your job. Do you stop or drive on?

From papers in your late father's desk you discover not only that you were adopted but that there is something you'd probably rather not know about your natural parents. You have had a happy life. Would you try to trace your natural parents?

You are desperate for money. For £20,000, would you have your darling and healthy dog or cat put down?

For fives times your annual income, would you be prepared to stay for five years in Central London or the Outer Hebrides? Strictly no travelling. Which?

If you knew you would receive truthful answers, what three questions would you ask about yourself and to whom would you put them?

If you knew you would receive truthful answers, what three questions would you ask your lover, spouse or best friend?

You are at last feeling fairly comfortably off. A woman turns up on your doorstep claiming (and she can prove it) to be your sister given up for adoption at birth by your late parents. She has had a dreadful life and is poverty stricken. Do you provide for her? And, if so, for how long?

You discover that the child you irresponsibly gave up for adoption 20 years ago and have not seen since is now a pop star. You genuinely want to see her despite possible recriminations but, being broke, don't want to seem grasping. Do you contact her?

A druggy friend has been round, and £40 is missing from the house. You think he must be the culprit but are not certain. Do you ring and confront him?

Your discover that your father, from whom you have inherited the family house and land, was not your grandfather's son. The rightful new owner is your first cousin, whom you are fond of and who has always loved the house. He lives in straitened circumstances in Hendon. Do you tell him the truth?

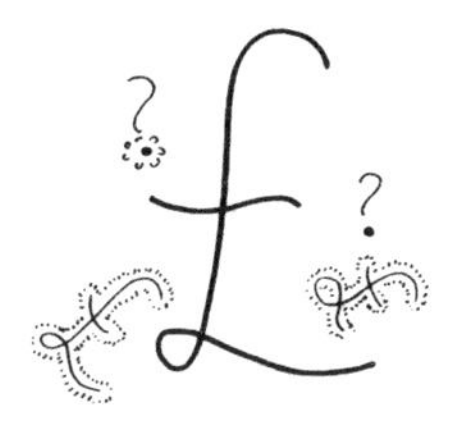

Your best friend is in a clinic with a serious alcohol and drug problem. He rings you halfway through his treatment and begs you to collect him. You know he has the means to discharge himself anyway but are not certain he will. You also know a refusal will sour your relationship. Do you?

After treatment in a clinic your ex-alcoholic but now cured best friend comes round for dinner and asks for a drink. A refusal may offend bitterly. Do you give him one?

Your reformed ex-alcoholic aunt comes to stay and smugly refuses all drinks. The next day you find an empty bottle of vodka hidden under her bed. It must be hers. Do you mention it next time you see her?

You walk into a room to find your fifteen-year-old niece snorting cocaine. Do you intervene? Do you tell her parents, who are strictly anti-drugs?

You are caught snorting cocaine by your nineteen-year-old niece. She asks you for a line. Knowing her parents are strictly anti-drugs, do you oblige?

At a huge party full of rich people you find £1,000 in an envelope on the gravel. Do you take it?

An acquaintance drops a lottery ticket which you realize is worth £10,000. Knowing he needs the money as much as you, do you hand it back?

Everything is getting out of hand at a stag party and someone rings for some tarts. One of them turns out to be a good friend's wife. She recognised you and leaves immediately. Do you ring her subsequently to discuss the incident or just never mention it? Do you tell your friend?

Your beloved, elderly, recently-widowed and lonely father wants to drive your ten-year-old son to a remote part of France, accessible only by road, for a fishing holiday. Your son is longing to go, but your father is an appalling driver, especially on foreign roads. Do you give your consent?

You are strongly attracted to your best friend's wife and know she is looking for an affair. Do you proceed?

You are strongly attracted to your boss's husband and know he is available. Do you proceed?

You have failed your driving test, essential for a wonderful new job, for the seventh time. A friend offers to take it for you. Do you let her?

You are very drunk in a remote country house. Your best friend, who lives 15 miles away, rings to say she is suicidal and pleads for you to go over. The only way to get there is to drive. You fear for her well-being, but it is a dreadful night and you are seeing triple. Do you go?

A very drunken guest is determined to drive home. Do you let him?

At a party, unseen, you stumble heavily and knock a priceless vase off a table. Do you own up, blame someone else or deny all knowledge?

At a dinner party, you've been holding forth about the ghastliness of a particular individual when you realize his wife is present. Do you backtrack, apologize, bluff it out, or leave?

At a lunch, you have been having fun ridiculing a book/exhibition/record when you realize the author/artist/artiste is present. Do you backtrack, apologize, bluff it out or leave?

Your business partner has told you something which will destroy a good friend unless he is made aware of it. If you tell the friend, your own business will be badly damaged. What do you do?

After a particularly acrimonious divorce, your best friend's ex-wife is still making his and his new wife's life hell. She – the ex – whom you have always been fond of, invites you to dinner. Do you go?

An old friend has been locked in a loveless marriage for many years and envisages his last chance of happiness in running off with another woman, an act that will devastate his wife and badly upset his children. He asks your advice. What do you tell him?

Your best friends' beloved child is horribly spoilt and ruins any social occasion. Do you tell them so?

You find a friend's child being very cruel to a dog. After giving him a serious bollocking, do you go on to tell his parents, knowing that they will be mortally offended?

You suspect your next door neighbours, with whom you are on friendly terms, of bashing their children, but you are not certain. Do you confront them, report them, or do nothing? What about if you suspect him of beating her?

Would you convert to a religion you disapprove of for the man you love?

Your best friend asks your advice. She is passionately in love with a wildly attractive but notoriously fickle restaurateur who will no doubt make her deliriously happy for a while but will almost certainly leave her in time. On the other hand a dull but kind and rich landowner is mad about her and has begged her to marry him. This would mean living in an isolated area of the country. What do you tell her?

A good friend has been left by her man and 9 months later is still ringing you snivelling at all hours. Do you tell her to pull herself together?

Your husband suggests inviting to dinner a girl from work to whom, you suspect, he is strongly attracted. You have never met her. Do you agree? If so, how do you behave to her? With over-friendliness? With indifference? With iciness?

At your lunch party, a good friend, who is an incorrigible snob, is making life difficult for a new friend of yours who is looking increasingly uncomfortable. Do you intervene? If so, how?

Though you don't like yourself for it, you are irresistibly attracted to celebrities. At a large party you get chatting to an American film star and find yourself inviting him to dinner. He accepts politely and suggests you call his office. Do you persevere?

At a smart dinner party with people you don't know well, the wine has been flowing like cement. After 45 minutes with an empty glass, do you ask for more?

Your best friend is treating his wonderful wife appallingly, with drunkenness, womanizing and the rest. Do you take her side?

Your host, who has it in his power to give you the job you crave, is being unpardonably rude to another guest who evidently can't stand up for herself. Do you intervene?

At dinner, your wife has been mildly insulted by your tipsy boss. She doesn't like him anyway and wants you to leave with her. Do you?

While playing the Truth Game, you are asked a question to which the answer will badly damage a friend. Do you lie?

Would you let your seventeen-year-old son sleep with a physically precocious fifteen-year-old? What about your nephew or godson?

A dear friend aged 60 asks himself for the weekend with his new girlfriend. To your horror she turns out to be the sixteen-year-old daughter of your godmother. Do you put them in the same room, as they obviously expect?

Your husband with whom you are deeply in love joins a cult. You don't like cults, particularly this one, but he begs you to become a member too. Do you?

You discover that your father has been systematically embezzling the funds of old ladies. The amounts have been small but consistent, and you too have gained. Would you report him? What if it were your husband?

You are an old-fashioned leftie. Your teenage son joins an extreme right-wing movement and wants to have his mates round all the time. Do you let him?

Your adored husband joins an extreme right-wing party and wants to ask the leader for the weekend. Do you agree?

You lose your wedding ring, worth £2,000, and claim insurance. A year later it turns up in a wellington boot. Do you inform the insurance company?

You find your best friend, a mother of children herself, in bed with your sixteen-year-old son? How would you react? What about if you found her in bed with your sixteen-year-old daughter?

You find your best friend, father of children himself, in bed with your sixteen-year-old daughter. How would you react? What about if you found him in bed with your sixteen-year-old son?

To be with the person you adore most, would you move to a far distant country knowing you could never see any of your friends and family again?

You are offered one year of complete happiness of which you would afterwards remember nothing. Would you take it?

You are informed that, due to a mistake in the hospital, your adored and perfect one-year-old child is not your own. Would you want to rectify the error? What if your real child was blemished in some way?

Would you rather be unattractive but rich or charming and beautiful but impoverished?

Would you embark upon the perfect affair if you knew your lover would die in six months? What if you knew instead that he would betray you in six months?

Your daughter has two best school chums, one the daughter of an affluent friend of a friend, the other the daughter of an unemployed bricklayer. Do you favour the former over the latter?

Your son is being bullied by one of his classmates. You know his mother is poor and single and finds it difficult to cope with him and life in general. Do you report him?

At a drinks party you are horrified to be introduced to a man who, many years ago at school, was a terrible bully, making the lives of a couple of your friends utterly miserable. Do you draw a veil over the past, remind him of it, cut him dead, or hit him?

Talking to a woman at a party you discover she is married to the office bully, who makes life miserable for you and your colleagues. Do you tell her?

Your best friend is dying painfully and asks you to put him out of his misery. Do you do so? What if you were to be prosecuted?

A good friend asks you to lend him £2,000. You are pretty certain you will never see the money again but thoroughly enjoy his company. Do you lend it?

You lend a friend more than you can afford and don't hear from him. You suspect he is avoiding you but miss his company. Do you ring him?

Your brother, who has inherited the family home, makes you unwelcome because of your small, rumbustious children. You did your fair share of babysitting his children. He invites himself to stay in your London flat with his tiresome wife. Do you say yes?

You live in a crumbing stately home with the trappings of wealth but have a vast overdraft. Your friends come to stay endlessly and eat and drink with gusto. Do you ask them to bring things?

You have been asked to stay by some rich friends. You are sent to the butcher to pick up the Sunday joint for twenty-two people. It costs a fortune and, despite you leaving the bill in a prominent place, your hosts fail to pay you back. Do you mention it?

You are desperate for money and know that a rich friend would lend you enough to get you out of trouble. You also know that he would never want to see you again, even after you have paid him back. Do you ask him for it?

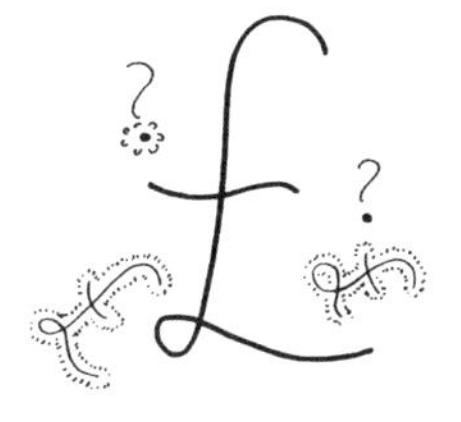

A friend splits up with her husband. Over a few drinks you tell her you always thought he was a complete creep anyway. A month later, when they are back together, he mentions the matter. Do you backtrack, apologize, or stick to your guns?

Would you lie in court for your best friend?

If, at birth, you could choose the profession of your child, would you?

Friends of friends are house-sitting for you for two weeks. It is a nice country break for them. You arrive back to find no staples – your supplies of pasta, rice and tinned fish have all gone. Do you remonstrate?

Your friend is an addictive gambler, something you disapprove of, especially because it makes life for his family very difficult. You know he has just lost £500 on a horse, and he asks you for a loan. Do you oblige?

Your friend has asked you to lunch to meet someone she is sure you will get on famously with. You dislike him on sight and disagree with everything he says. For your friend's sake do you smile politely, or do you bare your teeth and growl?

A once very dear friend now irritates you beyond all endurance. Do you still have her to stay, for old times' sake, or do you give her up?

A dear friend has married an odious creep. Do you still see them?

Do you ask your batty, incontinent aunt to the wedding?

You go to bed with two girls in quick succession and contract VD soon afterwards. The first is the girl of your dreams to whom you have professed complete loyalty. The second was a one night stand who denies being infected. Do you inform the first of your condition?

Would you flirt with your unattractive married boss for quick advancement?

Would you sleep with your unattractive married boss if it meant promotion and success?

In a position of power, would you favour your nephew or niece over another, better-qualified contender?

Your fiancé is fond of making jokes when out to dinner. They are not funny. Do you tell him so at the risk of great offence?

Your best friend's wife, who unwisely fancies herself as a singer, offers to perform at your wedding. You fear laughter in the aisles. Do you accept?

As a singular honour you are asked by your mother-in-law to open the dancing with her at her wedding anniversary, but your dancing is deplorable and you know you will embarrass both of you. You are allowed no excuses. Do you accept or decline?

You are going to a charity ball with your very rich friend. When you stupidly say that you have nothing to wear she buys you an expensive but hideous dress. Do you wear it?

Your charming but touchy great-uncle, whom you are attempting to butter up, asks you to dinner. You notice that the frozen moules marinières are a year past their sell-by date. Do you risk food poisoning not to offend him?

Your charming old father-in-law makes a drunken pass at you. Do you tell your husband?

Your well-preserved mother-in-law makes a pass at you. Do you tell your wife?

During her third martini, your mother-in-law tells you she has never liked her son, your husband. Do you tell him?

You discover that an amusing new friend is deeply malicious. Do you drop her?

Your best friend's new boyfriend makes a pass at you. Do you tell her?

You drink too much. Are you honest about the amount to your doctor, spouse, lover, family and best friend?

You have sworn to keep a friend's secret, knowledge of which would make your brother £50,000. Do you renege? The friend would never speak to you again.

A friend arrives to stay with his girlfriend. You put them in the same room. You discover the 'girlfriend' is his sister. Do you chuck them out?

A computer error credits your bank account with £5,000 that is not yours. Do you alert the bank to its mistake?

In the video-hire shop you find a bundle of money in the 'Classics' rack. No one would see you take it. Do you?

You are selling your flat to a sweet elderly couple. The snag is that your neighbours are terrors, specializing in all-night parties and hair-raising drunken rows. Do you tell your buyers?

You are selling your house to friends of friends. Though it has passed the survey, you know the roof leaks. Do you tell them?

If you could kill painlessly five starving peasants in China to cure a child you know of a horrible disease, would you do so?

By sticking four pins in a voodoo doll you can kill four prominent world politicians of whom you strongly disapprove. Would you do so? Who would you choose? If you could choose any four public figures, who would they be?

You are told that you will live to a great age and can either stay physically attractive or mentally alert. Which would you choose?

You are about to die. Spouse or lover excepted, who would you ring?

Which do you value most, professional success or a happy private life?

What ability or quality do you most lack? Would you rather lose faith, hope or charity to gain that ability?

You are extremely rich, and your family are expecting a good whack when you die. Someone approaches you with a cure for Aids which will need your entire fortune to succeed. What do you do?

Is there anyone you know with whom you would swop lives?

Would you murder your friend's innocent child (with no chance of being prosecuted) to create lasting world peace?

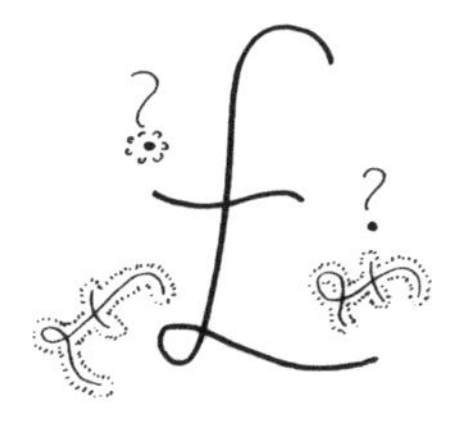

Is there anyone you know you hate enough to want to destroy?

Would you rather be given £10,000 for your own use or £100,000 to distribute magnanimously amongst your friends?

You have inside information that the world will end in six months and are given the power to achieve one previously unattainable goal. What would it be?

If you could excel at something, what would it be?

Your beloved fiancé is paralysed from the waist down in a climbing accident. Mountaineering and sex were the great bonds between you. Do you marry him?

Your house catches fire and you have time to rescue only one possession. What would it be?

What is your worst phobia? Would you spend one night confronting that phobia for one night with the woman of your dreams?

You are at a house party where most of the other guests are unknown to you. A good friend gets tight and spends the evening telling embarrassing tales about you to enormous laughter and acclaim. As her star waxes, so yours wanes, and you are left feeling worthless and humiliated, suspecting you will be the butt of many a joke for years to come. A week later your friend rings you. She is double-locked into her lover's flat with the wife's arrival imminent. You have a key. Do you rally round?

Would you give up sex for 5 years if you knew you would be permanently rich and happy afterwards?

You and your beloved are being held hostage. Your captors give you a choice. Either you or he may go free. Whoever stays will be killed. What is your decision?

Your best friend is in desperate need of a kidney. Would you donate one knowing your chances of a full recovery are only 50 per cent?

Would you live with insomnia for the rest of your life in exchange for £5 million?

You could have the perfect couple looking after you, your house and family forever, for free, but would never be able to entertain. Would you want them?

You are an enthusiastic carnivore, but in order to continue eating meat you have to go to a slaughter-house and kill a calf. Would you do so?

How much money would you require not to have contact with another living soul for a year, radio, television and Internet included?

Your best friend and her child, who is unlikely to reach maturity, fall overboard. You only have time to save one of them. Which?

In a position of power and distinction, you uncover a major racket. By exposing it you can save the lives of several people, but you will be unfairly implicated and go to your grave in disgrace. Do you do so?

How often do you give money on the street? Do you have a bias against drunks? Does a babe in arms soften your heart? Do you buy the *Big Issue*?

Your have a 75 per cent chance of increasing your wealth five-fold. If you lose, you lose everything you have. Do you take the bet?

Your ghastly mother-in-law has become incontinent and practically immobile. If you ask her to come and live with you you will benefit greatly from her large fortune, but she may last another ten years. Do you take her in?

While dining with your boss and her husband you find a decaying rodent in the casserole. You fear you may all be poisoned. Do you tell them?

Your odious boss is about to show some American investors round the factory when you notice his flies are gaping. Do you tell him?

A gold lighter has gone missing at a lunch party. By a process of elimination your hostess narrows it down to you. Deeply offended, you deny it hotly and leave the house in high dudgeon. A week later you find your child playing with it. Feelings are still running high, and letters have been exchanged. Do you ring and admit your mistake?

You and your boss have been swimming at the health club. You leave first. When back at the office you realize you have put on her knickers by mistake. On her return she says nothing. Do you?

You are forced to give your newborn child one of the seven deadly sins. Which do you choose? Does it make a difference if it's a boy or a girl?

If you could look like one of your friends, who would it be? Who wouldn't it be?

You are happily married and meet the man of your dreams. You know he will bring you lasting bliss. Do you run off with him? What if you have children?

Would you be confined to a wheelchair from 17 to 21 if this would guarantee you a happy and healthy rest of your life?

You have a chance of killing, legally and with your own hand, your best friend's murderer. Would you do so?

You have the chance of publicly humiliating someone who has done you a bad turn. Do you take it?

Some people you know only slightly have invited you and your family to lunch. You arrive with a bedraggled bunch of flowers from the garage and are greeted in opulent surroundings with lavish presents for your children, wonderful food and superb wines. You are broke and live in a small, grubby flat. Do you invite them back?

Your mother is terminally ill but doesn't want your father to know. He is about to spend a fortune on a no-money-refundable, round-the-world cruise as a surprise for her, which she won't live to enjoy. Do you tell him?

You are surprised to see your mother kissing a man passionately in Tesco's car-park. She catches your eye and begs you not to tell your father. You are equally fond of both parents and know that your father has been worried for some time that your mother is having an affair. What do you do?

Unknown to her, your wife is terminally ill. It has always been her life's ambition to finish her first novel, which you suspect may be very good, but she is only on Chapter 4. Do you tell her the bad news in order to hurry her up?

You are very shy. You are staying with some friends by the sea and they decide to go swimming in the nude. Do you join in?

You are at a country house weekend with a group of confident, clever, attractive young people. After dinner they suggest playing The Game. You are enthusiastically asked to join in, having been the life and soul of the party the night before, but you are now feeling shy and paranoid and know you will acquit yourself embarrassingly. Do you go through with it, in order not to be a killjoy, or take yourself to bed?

Your friend's nanny has told yours that your friend gives her hyperactive daughter surprisingly large quantities of gin to get her to sleep at night. Do you say anything to your friend?

You learn from your nanny that your friends' much treasured nanny is abusing their trust by having her boyfriend to stay in their bed every time they are away. Do you tell them?

Your wife suddenly announces she needs more excitement in her life and suggests 'swinging' with some willing acquaintances, or joining a 'partner-swap' club. Fearing a rift, do you consent?

You are successful. Do you tend to see less of your unsuccessful friends?

You are unsuccessful. Do you tend to see less of your successful friends?

On holiday, your best friend's new girlfriend turns out to be intolerably bossy. Do you tell him, her, both or neither?

A charming elderly couple are taking you out to an expensive restaurant for a treat. The service is shoddy and the food not up to scratch. Annoyed at your friends being taken for a ride, though they seem quite happy, do you intervene?

Arriving at the holiday villa with your friends, you are annoyed that they bag the best room, despite your seniority. Bearing in mind that you have two weeks together, do you object?

On holiday, your friends want to eat out with you every night. They drink considerably more than you and tend to order more expensive dishes. Do you demand financial adjustment?

In your house, a friendly game of poker becomes charged when a very rich guest, whose manners lack polish, suddenly ups the stake by £500. An impoverished guest, an inexperienced player who can't afford to lose, over-excitedly decides to 'see' him. Though to do so would ruin the game and probably the evening, do you intervene?

You have driven 15 miles to a dinner party given by new acquaintances whom you wish to impress. You are in evening dress and see through the window on arrival that they are in jeans and sweaters. At the risk of being inexcusably late, do you go home and change or bluff it out? What if you arrive in jeans and sweater to see them in evening dress?

You are dangerously merry after an excellent drinks party and have to go on to a sticky little dinner with people you need to impress. You may let yourself down badly. Do you bail out?

You are offered two jobs for life, one that you long for but which pays next to nothing, and another that bores you but pays handsomely. Which do you choose?

You find your child playing on a novelist friend's word processor and realize that she has deleted thirty-seven pages of the new *oeuvre*. Your friend has always been hopeless with his machine. Do you own up?

On your itemized telephone bill you notice the same mysterious number you don't recognize appearing five times. Do you ask your husband about it? Do you ring it?

During *Crimewatch* there is an appeal for the courting couple, seen kissing under a tree while a bank robber makes his getaway, to contact the police. The couple is you and your mistress. Do you dial the friendly inspector's number?

You are staying at a friend's house and he rings to ask you to check his telephone messages. You find one which can only be from his wife's drug dealer. Do you tell him?

On a sailing weekend with your boss and his wife on their boat, a storm blows up, and your boss, a less competent sailor than you, begins to lose his grip. At the risk of infuriating him, do you take the helm?

Would you be happy to be buried in an unmarked grave?

A good friend has been labouring over a novel in his spare time for years. The moment you have been dreading arrives: he has finished it and asks you to read it and give your honest opinion. It is dreadful, and no amount of editing can save it. Do you tell him so?

Would you be prepared to wear serious face jewellery – in eyebrow, nose, lip and lots in both ears – for one year, for £15,000? You are not allowed to explain your appearance.

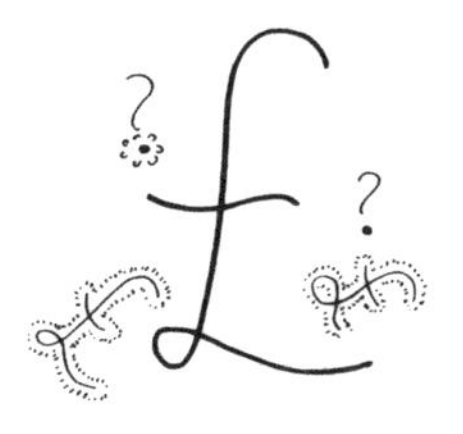

You are desperate for money. An unnattractive stranger approaches you at the gym and offers you £5,000 for a one night stand. Do you accept?

You have to spend the next two years in a prison cell and are allowed to choose the companion of your choice. Either sex allowed, but no spouses or lovers. Who would you choose?

For £500 would you unfairly and loudly abuse a waiter in a crowded restaurant? What if you were to split the money with him afterwards?

Would you be prepared to be facially disfigured for a fantastic house in the country?

Would you rather be deaf, dumb or blind?

You can marry a woman you adore and who will give you everything you desire except sex. Do you? No lovers allowed.

Would you steal £2,000 from a rich friend who wouldn't notice it to give to a deserving beggar at his door?

In a restaurant, celebrating with friends, you notice that an extremely expensive bottle of wine you have drunk does not appear on the bill. The mistake will almost certainly cost the very stroppy waitress her job. Do you correct the oversight?

On holiday in Devon your best friend, who is engaged to your rich uncle's daughter, has wrecked his future father-in-law's prized yacht. The disaster was due solely to his own drunkenness and recklessness, but he asks you, who were on board at the time, to take the rap. Do you, taking into account that you were hoping to inherit handsomely from your uncle?

Would you rather be simple and happy or brilliant but unhappy?

Do you stand up an old friend who is miserable and longing to talk things over, for a late invitation to a glamorous party?

Would you eat a plateful of cockroaches for £10,000? No alcohol or drugs allowed.

If a crystal ball could forecast your future, would you consult it?

How would you like to be perceived: nice but dull, or nasty but interesting?

Your kindly and generous boss has some very unpleasant personal habits. You don't want to hurt his feelings, but it is becoming unbearable to watch him picking his nose day after day. Do you say anything?

Your husband has taken up morris dancing. Do you leave him?

Your best friend is having a passionate affair with your ex-boyfriend. He chucked you only recently and you are still feeling rather hurt. They invite you to a terrific party. Do you go?

A friend of your husband's invites you to lunch at a delicious restaurant. You adore good food, but expect him to make an unwanted pass. Do you go? What if you go in good faith and he makes an unexpected pass halfway through, just when you are enormously looking forward to the chocolate soufflé? Do you leave?

You are getting married, and your best friend is desperate for you to include her children among your pages and bridesmaids. They are famously horrid and you expect them to ruin the service. Do you take the risk?

You are looking after a neighbour's young son's mouse while they are on holiday. It escapes. Do you buy a similar one and pass it off as the original, or do you own up?

Your ex-husband is cheating on his new wife. Do you tell her?

Your ex-husband's new wife is cheating on him. Do you tell him?

Your best friend is getting married to the sweetest girl on earth. You know he has recently had flings with two of her bridesmaids. Do you tell her?

You are at a dinner party and the wine has been flowing. Someone you find hugely attractive is making you reveal personal secrets and embarass your partner, by asking you questions from *The Delectable Book of Dilemmas*. Do you stay?